SEARCH A-PICTURE PUZZLES

kidsbooks
Incorporated

Published by KIDSBOOKS, Inc.
7004 N. California Ave.
Chicago, Illinois 60645 U.S.A.

ISBN: 0-942025-07-5

MANUFACTURED IN U.S.A.

How many clown hats can you find in the picture below? Count carefully because many of them overlap.

Solution on page 54

How many things are wrong with this picture? Find and circle them.

Solution on page 54

OPEN 10 - 4:30

ZOO

CLOSED 3 — 12:05

ELEFANT

Can you find these hidden objects in the picture below?

FORK   TEPEE
HEART   APPLE
FISH   KETTLE
FISH HOOK   SHOVEL
TOOTHBRUSH ROLLING PIN

Solution on page 55

TRICK OR TREAT

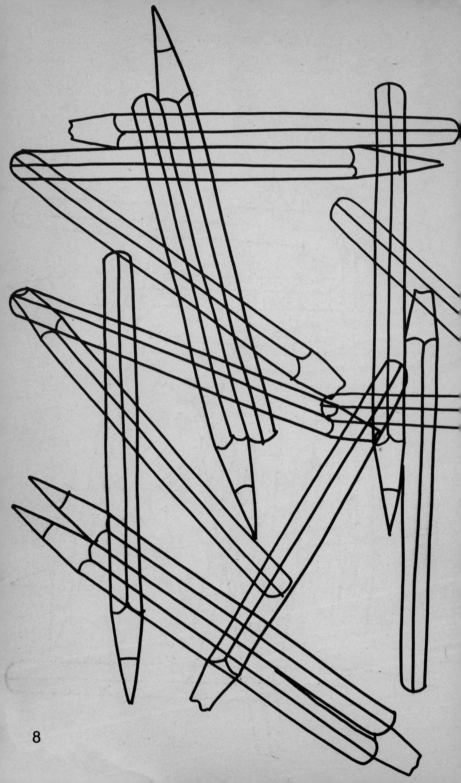

How many pencils with points can you count?
How many pencils with broken points can you count?

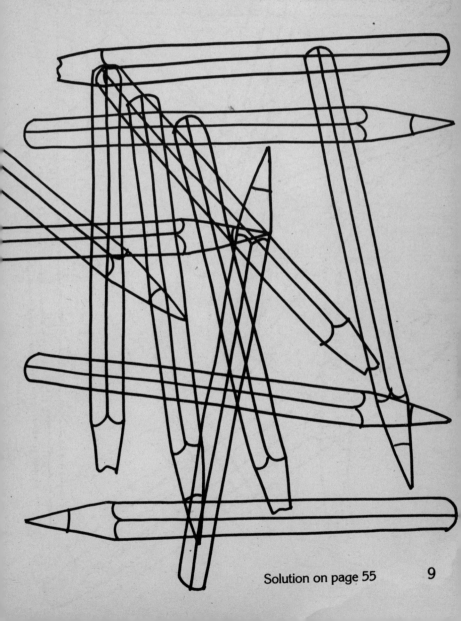

Solution on page 55

How many things that start with the letter "B" are in this picture? Find and circle them.

Solution on page 56

These pieces combine to make a picture. Copy the drawings from each numbered box into the box with the same number on the opposite page, and watch the picture come to life.

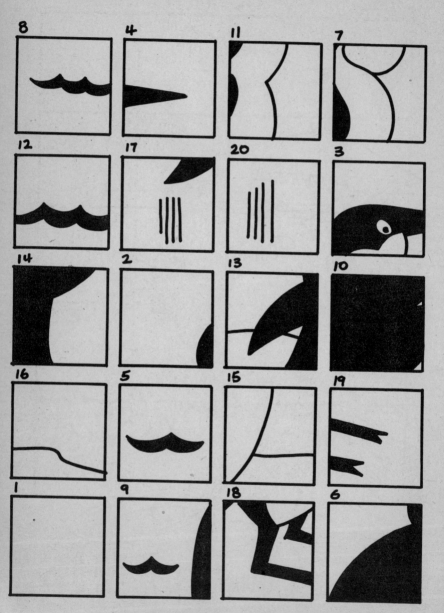

1	2	3	4
5	6	7	8
9	10	11	12
13	14	15	16
17	18	19	20

Solution on page 56

Compare these almost identical pictures. Then circle all of the places in the picture of the spacecraft on the right where something is either missing or different from the one on the left.

Solution on page 56

15

How many gulls can you count in this picture? Be careful, as many overlap.

Solution on page 57

These pieces combine to make a picture. Copy the drawings from each numbered box into the box with the same number on the opposite page, and watch the picture take form.

1	2	3	4
5	6	7	8
9	10	11	12
13	14	15	16
17	18	19	20

Solution on page 57

How many errors can you find in this picture? Circle
each one.

Solution on page 57

20

All of the letters of the alphabet have been hidden in this picture. Find and circle them.

Solution on page 58

23

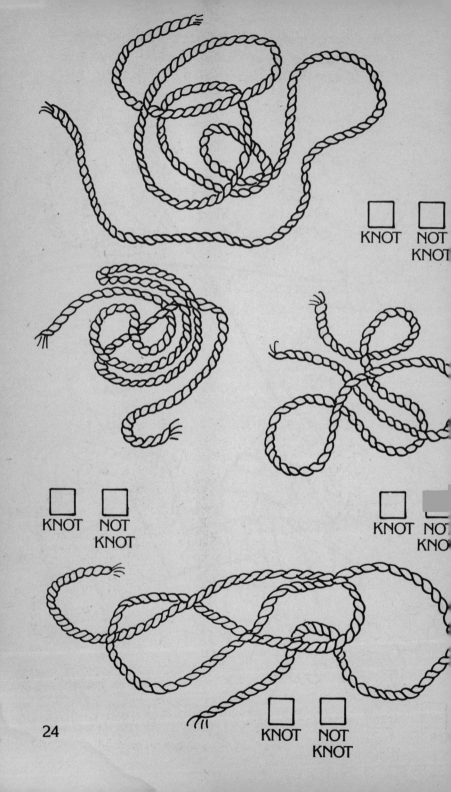

KNOT NOT KNOT

KNOT NOT KNOT

KNOT NOT KNOT

24

KNOT NOT KNOT

To knot, or not knot: that is the question. Carefully look at each rope and see if it would make a knot if the ends were pulled. Then mark the correct box.

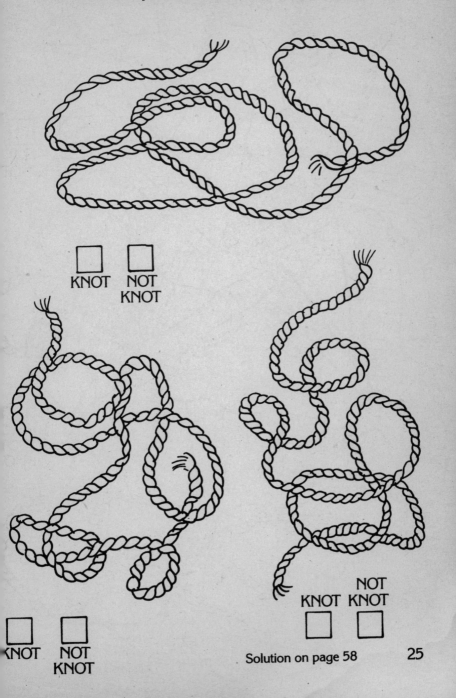

☐ KNOT   ☐ NOT KNOT

☐ KNOT   ☐ NOT KNOT

NOT
☐ KNOT   ☐ NOT KNOT

Solution on page 58

25

Find the following objects in this design:
STAR • HAT • HEART • KEY • PEN • SCISSORS •
CANDLE • CUPCAKE • APPLE • PEAR • KITE

26

Solution on page 59

Find and outline the 8 stars hidden below.

Solution on page 59

How many things can you find wrong with this disco scene?

Solution on page 59

28

These pieces combine to make a picture. Copy the drawings from each numbered box into the box with the same number on the opposite page, and watch the picture emerge.

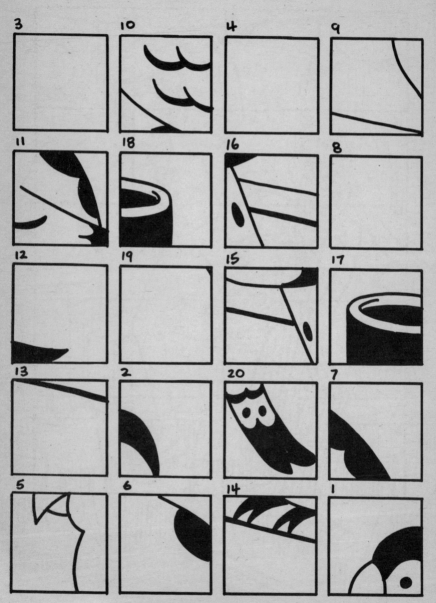

1	2	3	4
5	6	7	8
9	10	11	12
13	14	15	16
17	18	19	20

Solution on page 60

Compare these almost identical pictures. Then circle all of the places in the picture on the right where

something is either missing or different from the one on the left.

Solution on page 60

How many things that start with the letter "S" can you find in this picture?

Solution on page 60

How many things can you find wrong with this picture ?

Can you find these hidden objects in the picture below?

TOOTHBRUSH • FORK • SPOON • CUP • DRUM •
PEAR • KEY • PENCIL • TOP • PIG • ELEPHANT •
BLIMP • ROPE • GHOST • TENT • SEAL • CLOWN •
RING • HAND • BOOK • BIRD • BROOM • CANDLE

Solution on page 61

How many things can you find wrong in this baseball scene? Find at least 12 and you're safe. Under 12 and you're out! Find more than 15 and you're a home-run hitter!

Solution on page 62

These pieces combine to make a picture. Copy the drawings from each numbered box into the box with the same number on the opposite page, and watch the picture come to life.

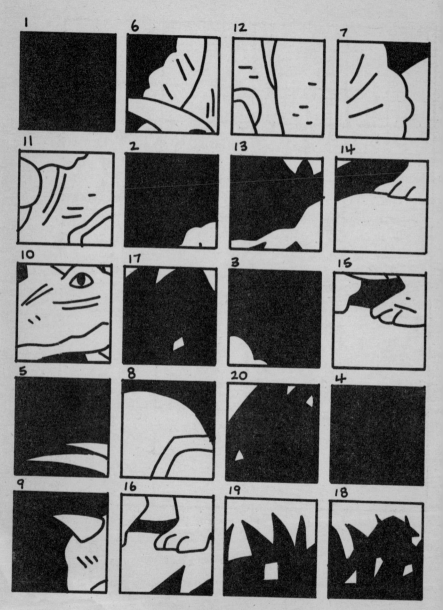

1	2	3	4
5	6	7	8
9	10	11	12
13	14	15	16
17	18	19	20

Solution on page 62

Compare these almost identical pictures, then circle all of the places in the picture on the right where something is either missing or different from the one on the left.

Help Sherlock find the following clues:

ENVELOPE • KNIFE • STAMP • GLOVE • BOW •
MIRROR • ARROW • CAP • BOOK • PEN •
SCISSORS • COMB • BRUSH

Solution on page 63

Can you find these objects hidden in the picture below?

IGLOO • BAT • FOOTBALL • LAMP • ANCHOR • EAR • JUG • ROCKET • MAGNET • EYE • MUSHROOM • GHOST • TURTLE • KNIFE • FORK • CUP • BAT • TULIP • LIPS

Solution on page 63

Compare these almost identical pictures. Then circle all of the places in the picture on the right where something is either missing or different from the one on the left.

Solution on page 64

Does this picture look finished? You'll find a lot of things have been left out. Draw in as many missing pieces as you can find.

Solution on page 64

SOLUTIONS

Page 3

14 HATS

Page 5

Page 9

WITH POINTS   <u>15</u>
BROKEN POINTS   <u>11</u>

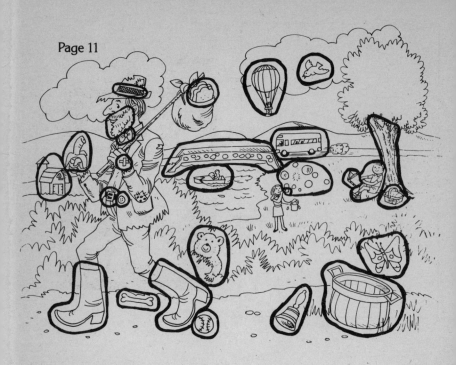

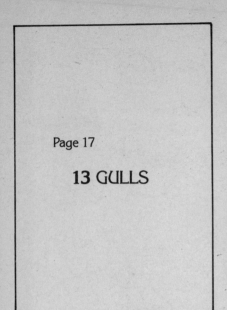

Page 17

13 GULLS

Page 19

Page 20

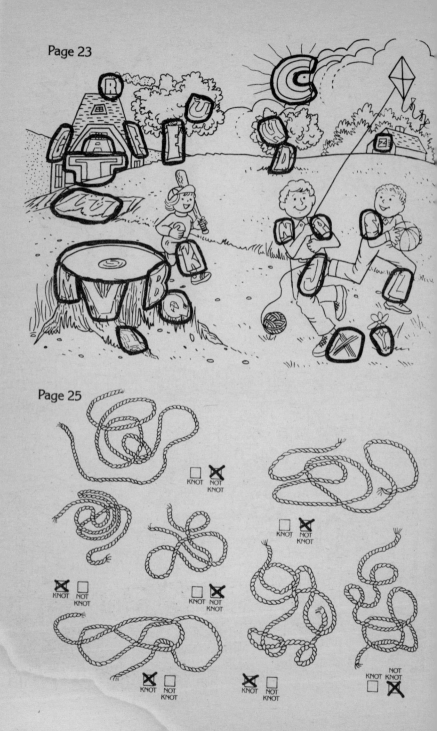

Page 23

Page 25

Page 26

Page 27

Page 28

Page 31

Page 33

Page 35

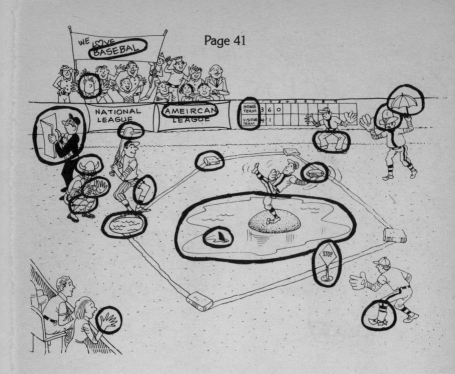

Page 47

Page 49